LOGIC NUMBER PROBLEMS
for Grades 4–8

Wade H. Sherard III

Dale Seymour Publications®
White Plains, New York

Special recognition and thanks are due to those fourth-, fifth-, and sixth-grade teachers and their students in the School District of Greenville County who tested the puzzles in this collection and to Michele C. Good for all of her help and expertise in preparing this manuscript for publication.

Managing Editor: Catherine Anderson
Production Manager: Janet Yearian
Project Editor: Joan Gideon
Production Coordinator: Joe Conte
Illustrations and Cover Art: Rachel Gage
Cover Design: Tracey Munz

Published by Dale Seymour Publications®, an imprint of
Addison Wesley Longman, Inc.

Dale Seymour Publications
10 Bank Street
White Plains, New York 10602
Customer Service: 800-872-1100

Order Number DS21195
ISBN 0-7690-0000-2

2 3 4 5 6 7 8 9 10-VG-01 00 99

Introduction for Teachers and Parents

More Logic Number Problems is a collection of 55 number puzzles designed to provide experiences in problem solving and mathematical reasoning for upper elementary school and middle school students. Each puzzle consists of a sequence of ten clues about an unknown number. The clues, when revealed one at a time, lead students through deductive reasoning to the discovery of the number. Because students need to know only basic definitions, concepts, and properties from arithmetic, numeration, and number theory to solve the puzzles, the primary emphasis is on problem-solving strategies and mathematical reasoning.

Learning to solve problems is one of the most important reasons for students at all levels to study mathematics. Critical-thinking skills developed through problem-solving activities in mathematics are useful for solving problems in many different disciplines. The National Council of Teachers of Mathematics in its *Curriculum and Evaluation Standards for School Mathematics* (1989) has set five general goals in mathematics for all K–12 students. Three of these goals are as follows:

1. Students should become mathematical problem solvers.
2. Students should learn to reason mathematically.
3. Students should learn to communicate mathematically.[1]

The National Council of Supervisors of Mathematics, in its position statement "Essential Mathematics for the Twenty-first Century" (1989), has also included problem solving, communicating mathematical ideas, and mathematical reasoning as three of its twelve components of essential mathematics.[2]

In recent years, greater emphasis has been placed on teaching problem solving and mathematical reasoning in the curriculum. Assessment studies show, however, that students' problem-solving skills are still considerably weaker than their computational skills. Clearly, more needs to be done to improve students' abilities to solve problems, reason mathematically, and think critically. Students especially need to be exposed to problem-solving activities in a variety of contexts.

The work of George Pólya has been a dominant influence on the teaching of problem solving in mathematics. Pólya recommends a four-phase procedure to provide structure and guidance in solving a problem.

Phase I:	Understanding the Problem
Phase II:	Devising a Plan
Phase III:	Carrying Out the Plan
Phase IV:	Looking Back

These four phases, and suggestions for implementing them, are discussed in detail in Pólya's books *How to Solve It* (first published in 1945) and *Mathematical Discovery*.[3] These books have had a tremendous impact on the teaching of problem solving. Analyses of articles, books, and current mathematics curricula concerning problem solving reveal many of Pólya's ideas, especially these four phases for solving a problem.

The second of Pólya's phases, devising a plan, is probably the most difficult for students. The following strategies for this phase (most of which are directly attributable to Pólya) are especially appropriate for solving the number puzzles in this collection.

1. Make a list of possibilities. Can the list be modified or reduced based on the conditions of the problem?
2. Carefully consider the conditions of the problem. What new information can be derived from the conditions? Are all the conditions necessary? Have all the conditions been taken into account?
3. Think of a related problem. Are there definitions or properties that are related to the unknowns, the data, and the conditions of the problem?
4. Consider a similar problem. Can its method of solution be used to solve this problem?
5. Search for patterns in the conditions or data. Is there a pattern that may be useful?
6. Try a guess-and-test approach; that is, an organized, systematic procedure of trial and error.

The puzzles in this collection provide students with ample opportunities to develop and use these problem-solving skills.

The fourth of Pólya's phases, looking back, is probably the most neglected phase in the teaching of problem solving, but it should be emphasized. The following are key questions to ask during this phase:

1. Is the answer reasonable? Does it make sense? Does the solution meet all the conditions of the problem? Can the solution be checked?
2. Is there another method for solving the problem? Is it shorter or more efficient? Is there another pattern of reasoning that leads to the solution?
3. Is this method of solution useful for other problems? Should the method of solution be remembered?

The puzzles in this collection provide students with many opportunities to ask these questions.

Pólya insists that the teaching of problem solving must include abundant experience in solving specific problems as well as careful study of the solution process itself. Students who solve, or attempt to solve, puzzles in this collection will gain valuable experience in solving problems, and with the appropriate guidance from their teacher, will begin to study the general process of problem solving.

Below are the basic definitions, concepts, and properties students need to know to solve these puzzles. These fundamental ideas from the arithmetic of whole numbers, numeration, and number theory are part of the standard mathematics curriculum for grades 4–8.

Arithmetic of Whole Numbers
- basic facts of addition, subtraction, multiplication, and division
- vocabulary related to addition, subtraction, multiplication, and division
- properties of the number 0 in addition, subtraction, and multiplication
- properties of the number 1 in multiplication and division

Numeration
- concepts of place value and face value
- comparison of numbers using face values and place values of their numerals
- patterns in the digits of numerals

Number Theory
- even and odd numbers
- divisors, factors, and multiples
- prime numbers
- prime factors of numbers
- divisibility tests for 2 and 5

The puzzles in this collection provide opportunities for students to master the basic facts of addition, subtraction, multiplication, and division; to learn important vocabulary related to computation; to reinforce understanding of place value and face value in numeration; and to develop skills in creating and recognizing patterns. Solving these puzzles helps students develop number sense while they develop skills in solving problems and reasoning mathematically. In addition, many of the clues expose students to the language of pre-algebra and algebra.

Sample Puzzles and Suggested Solutions

Each puzzle in this collection consists of a list of ten clues about a particular number. The clues are designed to be disclosed one at a time, with each new clue providing more information about the unknown number. The clues allow students to use deductive reasoning to determine the various digits of its numeral. The object of a puzzle is to discover the unknown number by using the least possible number of clues. Once the number has been determined, the remaining clues serve to confirm the solution. Solutions to the 55 puzzles in this book can be found on page 56. Below are three sample puzzles and suggested solutions.

Puzzle A

1. It is a four-digit whole number.

2. The sum of its hundreds digit and its ones digit is 7.

3. The sum of its thousands digit and its tens digit is 12.

4. The sum of its ones digit and its thousands digit is 9.

5. It is greater than 8000.

6. It has only one even digit.

7. Its ones digit is its smallest digit.

8. Its thousands digit is three times its tens digit.

9. Its hundreds digit is 7.

10. Its ones digit is 0.

Suggested Solution to Puzzle A by clues:

1. The number has the form

   ____ ____ ____ ____.

2. The possibilities for its hundreds digit and its ones digit are

7	0
6	1
5	2
4	3
3	4
2	5
1	6
0	7

   ____ ____ ____ ____

3. The possibilities for its thousands digit and its tens digit are

9	3
8	4
7	5
6	6
5	7
4	8
3	9

   ____ ____ ____ ____

2, 3, 4. Collectively, these clues allow us to make the following list of possible numbers:

   9730
   8641
   7552
   6463
   5374
   4285
   3196

5. The list is reduced to

   9370
   8641

6. The unknown number must be 9730.

7, 8, 9, 10. These conditions serve to confirm that 9730 is the solution to the puzzle.

Several problem-solving strategies from Pólya's second phase, devising a plan, are used to solve Puzzle A. The underlying strategy is that of making a list of possibilities. The new information revealed with each clue allows students to reduce the list of possibilities until the solution is easily determined. The conditions in the clues require students to consider definitions, concepts, and properties related to the unknown number. And, students must look for patterns in the digits of numbers to ensure that they generate a complete list of possible solutions after the fourth clue.

Not all of the clues are needed to solve this puzzle. The solution can be determined after clue 6. The remaining clues can be used to confirm the solution. After solving this or any other puzzle, it is important for students to ask the following questions: Is this answer reasonable? Does it make sense? Can this method of solution be used to solve other problems? Is there another way to derive the solution? These questions begin Pólya's fourth phase, looking back, an examination of the puzzle's solution.

Puzzle B
1. It is a five-digit whole number.
2. It is an odd number.
3. It is less than 15,000.
4. Its tens digit is greater than 7.
5. Its hundreds digit is a multiple of 7.
6. It has only three different digits.
7. The sum of all of its digits is 10.
8. None of its digits is a 7.
9. Its thousands digit is less than 2.
10. Its tens digit is 8.

Suggested Solution to Puzzle B by clues:
1. The number has the form

   ____ ____ , ____ ____ ____ .

2. Its ones digit must be 1, 3, 5, 7, or 9.
3. Its ten thousands and thousands digits as a pair must be 10, 11, 12, 13, or 14.
4. Its tens digit must be 8 or 9.
5. Its hundreds digit must be 0 or 7, since 0 x 7 = 0 and 1 x 7 = 7.

	4			9
	3			7
	2			5
	1	7	9	3
1	0	0	8	1
____	____ ,	____	____	____

Based on the first five clues, there are 100 possible solutions—too many to list.

6. Using the fact that the number has only three different digits, the following list can be generated.

10,081	11,781
10,091	11,787
10,099	11,791
11,081	11,797
11,091	11,799
11,099	

7. The unknown number must be 10,081, since it is the only number on the list whose digits add to 10.

8, 9, 10. These conditions serve to confirm that 10,081 is the solution to the puzzle.

As with Puzzle A, the key problem-solving strategy for Puzzle B is that of making a list of possibilities and reducing the list based on the clues. Using patterns is another important problem-solving strategy for this puzzle. By using patterns, students can conduct a systematic search to find all the possible numbers that satisfy clues 1 through 6. Students who instead use a haphazard trial-and-error approach may overlook potential candidates for the solution. This is a good point to discuss in the looking-back phase of this puzzle's solution.

Puzzle C
1. It is a three-digit whole number.
2. The product of all of its digits is 18.
3. The product of two of its digits is 6.
4. Two of its digits are odd.
5. It is an even number.
6. It is greater than 300.
7. Its even digit is its greatest digit.
8. It is less than 600.
9. Each of its digits is different.
10. Its ones digit is 6.

Suggested Solution to Puzzle C by clues:
1. The number has the form ____ ____ ____ .

2. Since 18 = 1 x 2 x 9 or 18 = 1 x 3 x 6 or
   18 = 2 x 3 x 3, its possible digits are 1, 2, 9
   or 1, 3, 6 or 2, 3, 3.

3. Now its possible digits are 1, 3, 6 or 2, 3, 3,
   which leads to this brief list of possible
   numbers.

136	233
163	323
316	332
361	
613	
631	

4. This clue is redundant.

5. The list can now be reduced to

136	332
316	

6. The list is further reduced to

316	332

7. The unknown number must be 316.

8, 9, 10. These conditions serve to confirm
   that 316 is the solution to the puzzle.

As in Puzzle B, using patterns is important in
solving Puzzle C, particularly when listing the
possible solutions based on the first three clues.
Using patterns is critical when undertaking a
systematic search for all the possible solutions
to a puzzle because it ensures that the trial-
and-error process is organized, thorough, and
complete.

According to Pólya , students must have experience not only in solving problems, but in study-
ing the process of solving problems. During
Pólya's fourth phase, looking back, students
should always ask these questions: Can this
method of solution be used to solve other puzzles? If so, should it be remembered? Is there
another way to solve the puzzle? Is there a
better method?

Looking back gives students a basis for develop-
ing plans for solving other problems. When students are faced with a new problem, they can
use what they have learned from looking back at
other solutions to help them answer these questions: Have I solved a similar problem? Can the
solution method from that problem be used to

solve this problem? Each puzzle in this collection
has at least one "parallel," or "companion," puzzle that can be solved by the same method. This
helps students learn the value of reusing specific
solution strategies in appropriate situations.

Algebraic Thinking

The puzzles in this book provide students with
opportunities to engage in algebraic thinking.
Algebra can be viewed as a language for express-
ing mathematical relationships. The language
about unknowns and the relationship among
them used in many of the clues is the language
of algebra. (The unknowns, or variables, in a
puzzle are the digits of the place values of the
number that is the solution.) Students engage in
algebraic thinking when they use clues such as
the following:

- The sum of its tens digits and its hundreds
  digits is 8.
- The quotient of its hundreds digit and its
  ones digit is 6.
- Its tens digit is a factor of 9.
- Its hundreds digit is less than its tens digit.

Clues such as these are the English equivalents
of algebraic expressions, equations, and inequal-
ities, and finding all the possible digits that satisfy them requires algebraic thinking.

Several clues require students to apply algebraic
properties. For example, the clue "The product of
all of its digits is 0." requires students to conclude that at least one of its digits is 0. The clue
"The quotient of its hundreds digit and its tens
digit is 1." requires students to conclude that the
hundreds digit and the tens digit are the same
nonzero number. Both of these examples involve
algebraic thinking.

Some of the puzzles require students to look for
patterns, another aspect of algebraic thinking.
For example, students may need to generate all
the numbers that satisfy the first several clues in
a puzzle. To do this successfully, they must iden-
tify patterns that allow them to list systematically
all the numbers satisfying the information in
those clues.

In solving these puzzles, students use their knowledge of numbers, number properties, and arithmetic to engage in algebraic thinking and to build meaning for the symbols and operations they will learn later when they study algebra more formally.

Suggestions for Using the Puzzles

The puzzles in this collection vary in difficulty. Some are straightforward and routine, while others are more challenging and thought-provoking, requiring greater creativity and insight. The more difficult puzzles appear in the latter part of the book. When deciding whether a particular puzzle is appropriate for a particular group of students, consider their mathematical background and level of achievement. Since the mathematical prerequisites for solving the puzzles are minimal, most of the puzzles are appropriate for upper elementary school students and middle school students.

This book may be used in school or at home. The puzzles can be solved by students working individually or in small groups. Since the objective of the puzzle is to determine the unknown number by using the least number of clues, assessment of students' work should be based not only on a solution's correctness, but on the number of clues used to find the solution. Of course, students should understand that the clues are to be disclosed one at a time and considered sequentially.

The puzzles can be used in competitive game situations. For example, you might divide the class into teams of students, and uncover the clues to a puzzle one at a time using an overhead projector. When a team thinks they have found the solution, they can write it and the number of the last clue they used to determine it on a slip of paper. A possible scoring scheme is:

+1 for determining the unknown number

+2 for correctly stating the number of the clue at which the solution can first be determined

+1 for stating a clue number that is one greater than the clue number at which the solution can first be determined

–2 for giving an incorrect solution (This penalty is meant to discourage premature guessing.)

If only a few teams are involved in the competition, points could also be awarded to the team that first determines the correct solution.

Regardless of how you use the puzzles, take the time to discuss the solutions and the problem-solving strategies with students. This important aspect of teaching problem solving will help students develop good problem-solving and reasoning skills. By providing careful, deliberate discussion of the problem-solving process, you can serve as a role model for students to emulate as they grow into successful problem-solvers.

---

1 NCTM, *Curriculum and Evaluation Standards for School Mathematics.* (Reston, VA: NCTM, 1989), pp. 5–6.

2 NCSM, "Essential Mathematics for the Twenty-first Century," *Mathematics Teacher 82* (September 1989), pp. 470–74.

3 Pólya , George. *How to Solve It,* 2nd ed. (Princeton, NJ: Princeton University Press, 1973), p. 172; *Mathematical Discovery,* combined edition. (New York: John Wiley & Sons, 1981).

Puzzle 1

1. It is a three-digit whole number.

2. It is an odd number.

3. It is greater than 500.

4. One of its digits is 4.

5. Its hundreds digit is the sum of its tens digit and its ones digit.

6. The sum of its hundreds digit and its ones digit is 6.

7. Its tens digit is 1 less than its hundreds digit.

8. It is less than 600.

9. The difference between its tens digit and its ones digit is 3.

10. Its ones digit is 1.

Puzzle 2

1. It is a four-digit whole number.

2. The sum of its tens digit and its ones digit is 10.

3. The sum of its hundreds digit and its tens digit is 9.

4. The sum of its thousands digit and its hundreds digit is 8.

5. It is less than 3000.

6. It is an odd number.

7. Its ones digit is its largest digit.

8. Its hundreds digit is twice its tens digit.

9. Its tens digit is 3.

10. Its thousands digit is 2.

Puzzle 3

1. It is a four-digit whole number.

2. Its tens digit is its smallest digit.

3. Its thousands digit is three times its tens digit.

4. Its hundreds digit is the sum of its thousands digit and its tens digit.

5. It is divisible by 5.

6. Its ones digit is its largest digit.

7. It has only one even digit.

8. It is less than 5000.

9. Its hundreds digit is 4.

10. Its tens digit is 1.

Puzzle 4

1. It is a three-digit whole number.

2. It is greater than 800.

3. Its hundreds digit is the sum of its tens digit and its ones digit.

4. It is less than 900.

5. All of its digits are even.

6. Two of its digits are the same.

7. One of its digits is 0.

8. Its ones digit is the sum of its tens digit and its hundreds digit.

9. Its ones digit is 8.

10. Its tens digit is 0.

Puzzle 5

1. It is a four-digit whole number.

2. Its hundreds digit and its tens digit are the same.

3. Its thousands digit and its ones digits are the same.

4. It is an even number.

5. The sum of its hundreds digit and its tens digit is 16.

6. The sum of all of its digits is 28.

7. All of its digits are even.

8. It is greater than 6000.

9. Its hundreds digit is 8.

10. Its ones digit is 6.

Puzzle 6

1. It is a four-digit whole number.

2. The product of its hundreds digit and its tens digit is 6.

3. The product of its thousands digit and its ones digit is 14.

4. Two of its digits are the same.

5. The product of its tens digit and its ones digit is 21.

6. It is an odd number.

7. It is less than 3000.

8. The product of its thousands digit and its hundreds digit is 4.

9. Its tens digit is 3.

10. Its hundreds digit is 2.

Puzzle 7

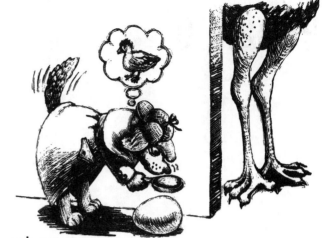

1. It is a three-digit whole number.

2. Its hundreds digit is less than its tens digit.

3. Its tens digit is less than its ones digit.

4. It is an even number.

5. Its tens digit divided by its hundreds digit is 7.

6. The product of two of its digits is 8.

7. It has only one even digit.

8. One of its digits is the sum of its other two digits.

9. One of its digits is 7.

10. Its hundreds digit is 1.

Puzzle 8

1. It is a three-digit whole number.

2. Its tens digit is an odd number.

3. It has exactly two different digits.

4. Its hundreds digit is a multiple of 4.

5. Its ones digit is an even number.

6. It is less than 800.

7. The sum of all of its digits is 17.

8. Its tens digit is 5 more than its hundreds digit.

9. Its ones digit is 4

10. Its tens digit is 9.

Puzzle 9

1. It is a four-digit whole number.

2. Its hundreds digit divided by its tens digit is 3.

3. Its thousands digit minus its ones digit is 8.

4. It has no even digits.

5. The sum of its thousands digit and its tens digit is 10.

6. Two of its digits are the same.

7. It is greater than 8000.

8. The sum of its tens digit and its ones digit is 2.

9. Its hundreds digit is 3.

10. Its thousands digit is 9.

Puzzle 10

1. It is a three-digit whole number.

2. Each of its digits is different.

3. Its ones digit is its only even digit.

4. Its tens digit is its smallest digit.

5. Its ones digit is its largest digit.

6. It is less than 500.

7. One of its digits is the sum of its other two digits.

8. The difference between its largest digit and its smallest digit is 3.

9. One of its digits is 4.

10. Its hundreds digit is 3.

Puzzle 11

1. It is a six-digit whole number.

2. It is greater than 800,000.

3. Its hundreds digit is the same as its thousands digit.

4. Its hundred thousands digit is twice its ones digit.

5. Its tens digit is the same as its hundred thousands digit.

6. Its tens digit is four times its hundreds digit.

7. It is an even number.

8. Its ten thousands digit is the same as its ones digit.

9. The sum of all of its digits is 28.

10. Its ones digit is 4.

Puzzle 12

1. It is a three-digit whole number.

2. Its hundreds digit is a factor of 3.

3. Its tens digit is a factor of 6.

4. Its ones digit is a factor of 9.

5. All of its digits are different.

6. Its hundreds digit is its smallest digit.

7. All of its digits are odd.

8. Its ones digit is divisible by its hundreds digit.

9. Its hundreds digit is 1.

10. Its tens digit is 3.

Puzzle 13

1. It is a three-digit whole number.

2. It is an even number.

3. It is less than 600.

4. One of its digits is a 7.

5. Its tens digit is the sum of its hundreds digit and its ones digit.

6. The difference between its hundreds digit and its ones digit is 1.

7. It is greater than 300.

8. Its tens digit is its largest digit.

9. The sum of its hundreds digit and its tens digit is 10.

10. Its ones digit is 4.

Puzzle 14

1. It is a four-digit whole number.

2. Its thousands digit is its smallest digit.

3. Its hundreds digit is four times its thousands digit.

4. Its tens digit is the sum of its thousands digit and its hundreds digit.

5. It is divisible by 5.

6. It has only one even digit.

7. Two of its digits are the same.

8. The quotient of its tens digit and its ones digit is 1.

9. Its tens digit is 5.

10. Its hundreds digit is 4.

Puzzle 15

1. It is a three-digit whole number.

2. It is less than 500.

3. Its hundreds digit is the sum of its tens digit and its ones digit.

4. All of its digits are even.

5. Two of its digits are the same.

6. One of its digits is 0.

7. It is greater than 300.

8. The sum of its hundreds digit and its tens digit is 8.

9. Its tens digit is 4.

10. Its ones digit is 0.

Puzzle 16

1. It is a four-digit whole number.

2. Its hundreds digit and its ones digit are the same.

3. Its thousands digit and its tens digit are the same.

4. The sum of its hundreds digit and its ones digit is 14.

5. The sum of all of its digits is 32.

6. It is not an even number.

7. It is greater than 7000.

8. All of its digits are odd.

9. Its tens digit is 9.

10. Its hundreds digit is 7.

Puzzle 17

1. It is a four-digit whole number.

2. The product of its hundreds digit and its ones digit is 8.

3. The product of its thousands digit and its tens digit is 5.

4. Each of its digits is different.

5. The product of its hundreds digit and its tens digit is 4.

6. It is an even number.

7. It is greater than 5000.

8. The product of its thousands digit and its ones digit is 10.

9. Its hundreds digit is 4.

10. Its ones digit is 2.

Puzzle 18

1. It is a three-digit whole number.

2. Its hundreds digit is greater than its tens digit.

3. Its tens digit is greater than its ones digit.

4. It is an odd number.

5. Its tens digit divided by its ones digit is 8.

6. The product of two of its digits is 9.

7. It has only one even digit.

8. One of its digits is the sum of its other two digits.

9. One of its digits is 8.

10. Its ones digit is 1.

Puzzle 19

1.   It is a three-digit whole number.

2.   Its tens digit is an even number.

3.   It has exactly two different digits.

4.   Its hundreds digit is a multiple of 3.

5.   Its ones digit is an odd number.

6.   It is greater than 700.

7.   Its tens digit is 1 less than its hundreds digit.

8.   The sum of all of its digits is 26.

9.   Its ones digit is 9.

10.   Its tens digit is 8.

Puzzle 20

1. It is a four-digit whole number.

2. Its hundreds digit minus its ones digit is 6.

3. Its thousands digit divided by its tens digit is 4.

4. It has no odd digits.

5. The product of its hundreds digit and its ones digit is 0.

6. It is greater than 8000.

7. Each of its digits is different.

8. Its thousands digit is the sum of its hundreds digit and its tens digit.

9. Its hundreds digit is 6.

10. Its ones digit is 0.

Puzzle 21

1. It is a three-digit whole number.

2. Its tens digit is its largest digit.

3. Its ones digit is its smallest digit.

4. Each of its digits is different.

5. Its ones digit is its only odd digit.

6. It is greater than 500.

7. The difference between its largest digit and its smallest digit is 5.

8. The sum of all of its digits is 17.

9. One of its digits is 3.

10. Its tens digit is 8.

Puzzle 22

1. It is a five-digit whole number.

2. Its hundreds digit is less than 2.

3. It is greater than 95,000.

4. Its tens digit is divisible by 5.

5. Each of its digits is different.

6. The sum of all of its digits is 17.

7. It is an even number.

8. Its ones digit is less than 3.

9. It has three odd digits.

10. Its thousands digit is 5.

Puzzle 23

1. It is a six-digit whole number.

2. It is less than 300,000.

3. Its hundreds digit is seven times its hundred thousands digit.

4. Its ones digit is the same as its thousands digit.

5. Its thousands digit is a multiple of 3.

6. Its ten thousands digit is the same as its hundreds digit.

7. Its thousands digit is 2 more than its hundreds digit.

8. Its tens digit is the same as its hundred thousands digit.

9. All of its digits are odd.

10. Its ones digit is 9.

Puzzle 24

1. It is a three-digit whole number.

2. Its hundreds digit is a factor of 8.

3. Its tens digit is a factor of 4.

4. Its ones digit is a factor of 2.

5. All of its digits are different.

6. Its tens digit is its only odd digit.

7. It is greater than 500.

8. Its hundreds digit is divisible by its ones digit.

9. Its tens digit is 1.

10. Its hundreds digit is 8.

Puzzle 25

1. It is a five-digit whole number.

2. Its ten thousands digit and its tens digit are the same.

3. Its thousands digit and its ones digit are the same.

4. It has only one 3.

5. The sum of its tens digit and its ones digit is 6.

6. The product of its thousands digit and its hundreds digit is 15.

7. All of its digits are odd.

8. It is less than 20,000.

9. Its hundreds digit is 3.

10. Its ones digit is 5

Puzzle 26

1. It is a six-digit whole number.

2. It has only two different digits, each used three times.

3. The product of its ones digit and its hundred thousands digit is 8.

4. It is an odd number.

5. The quotient of its tens digit and its hundred thousands digit is 1.

6. The sum of its thousands digit and its tens digit is 9.

7. The difference between its thousands digit and its hundreds digit is 0.

8. The difference between its ten thousands digit and its ones digit is 7.

9. The sum of its thousands digit and its hundreds digit is 2.

10. Its hundred thousands digit is 8.

Puzzle 27

1. It is a six-digit whole number.

2. Its only digits are 0 and 1.

3. The sum of all of its digits is 4.

4. It is divisible by 2.

5. The sum of its hundreds digit, its tens digit, and its ones digit is 2.

6. The quotient of its thousands digit and its hundreds digit is 1.

7. It is greater than 100,000.

8. The sum of its hundred thousands digit, its ten thousands digit, and its thousands digit is 2.

9. Its tens digit is 1.

10. Its ten thousands digit is 0.

Puzzle 28

1. It is a four-digit whole number.

2. Each of its digits is different.

3. The product of all of its digits is 64.

4. Its thousands digit is odd.

5. Its hundreds digit is the product of its tens digit and its ones digit.

6. It is an even number.

7. Its tens digit is less than its ones digit.

8. The sum of all of its digits is 15.

9. Its ones digit is 4.

10. Its thousands digit is 1.

Puzzle 29

1. It is a three-digit whole number.

2. Its tens digit is its largest digit.

3. The difference between its tens digit and its hundreds digit is 3.

4. Its ones digit is its only digit that is not divisible by 3.

5. Its hundreds digit is one-half of its tens digit.

6. It has a remainder of 1 when it is divided by 7.

7. It is an odd number.

8. The difference between its ones digit and its hundreds digit is 2.

9. It is divisible by 5.

10. Its tens digit is 6.

Puzzle 30

1. It is a three-digit whole number.

2. The product of all of its digits is 12.

3. The product of two of its digits is 6.

4. Two of its digits are even.

5. It is an odd number.

6. It is less than 600.

7. Its odd digit is its greatest digit.

8. It is greater than 200.

9. Two of its digits are the same.

10. Its ones digit is 3.

Puzzle 31

1. It is a six-digit whole number.

2. It has only one even digit.

3. It has only one odd digit.

4. It is an odd number.

5. It is less than 300,000.

6. It is greater than 280,000.

7. The quotient of its hundreds digit and its ones digit is 1.

8. Its digits alternate.

9. The difference between its ten thousands digit and its tens digit is 7.

10. Its thousands digit is 2.

Puzzle 32

1. It is a four-digit whole number.

2. Its ones digit is an odd number.

3. Its hundreds digit is one-third of its ones digit.

4. The product of all of its digits is 0.

5. Its thousands digit is the sum of its hundreds digit and its ones digit.

6. It has only two odd digits.

7. It is less than 5000.

8. The sum of all of its digits is 8.

9. Its tens digit is 0.

10. Its ones digit is 3.

Puzzle 33

1. It is a four-digit whole number.

2. It is less than 2000.

3. Each digit is less than the digit to its right.

4. Its tens digit is the sum of its thousands digit and its hundreds digit.

5. Its ones digit is the sum of its hundreds digit and its tens digit.

6. The product of its thousands digit and its ones digit is 7.

7. It has three odd digits.

8. The product of its thousands digit and its tens digit is 4.

9. Its ones digit is 7.

10. Its hundreds digit is 3.

Puzzle 34

1. It is a four-digit whole number.

2. The product of its hundreds digit and its ones digit is 0.

3. The product of its thousands digit and its tens digit is 5.

4. The product of its tens digit and its ones digit is 35.

5. It is an odd number.

6. Its tens digit is less than its ones digit.

7. Its tens digit is greater than its thousands digit.

8. The difference between its tens digit and its hundreds digit is 5.

9. It is less than 2000.

10. Its ones digit is 7.

Puzzle 35

1. It is a three-digit whole number.

2. None of its digits are the same.

3. One of its digits differs from each of its other two digits by 1.

4. Its ones digit is its smallest digit.

5. The difference between its tens digit and its ones digit is 2.

6. The product of its smallest digit and its largest digit is 24.

7. It has two even digits.

8. It is greater than 500.

9. Its ones digit is 4.

10. Its tens digit is 6.

Puzzle 36

1. It is a three-digit whole number.

2. Its remainder is 3 if it is divided by 5.

3. Its hundreds digit is a divisor of 14.

4. Its tens digit is 1 more than a multiple of 5.

5. It has no odd digits.

6. Its tens digit is the difference between its ones digit and its hundreds digit.

7. It is less than 700.

8. The sum of all of its digits is 16.

9. Its ones digit is 8.

10. Its tens digit is 6.

Puzzle 37

1. It is a five-digit whole number.

2. It is divisible by 2.

3. It is greater than 40,000.

4. It is less than 44,000.

5. None of its digits are odd.

6. It has only two different digits.

7. The sum of all of its digits is 8.

8. Its tens digit is less than its ones digit.

9. Its thousands digit is the sum of its hundreds digit and its tens digit.

10. Its hundreds digit is 0.

Puzzle 38

1. It is a four-digit whole number.

2. Its hundreds digit has exactly two factors.

3. Its thousands digit has exactly one factor.

4. Its ones digit has exactly four factors.

5. Its tens digit is the product of its thousands digit and its hundreds digit.

6. The sum of all of its digits is greater than 22.

7. It has only one even digit.

8. Two of its digits are the same.

9. Its ones digit is the sum of two of its other digits.

10. Its ones digit is 8.

Puzzle 39

1. It is a four-digit whole number.

2. It is a multiple of 25.

3. Its thousands digit is 3 more than its ones digit.

4. Its hundreds digit is 2 less than its tens digit.

5. Each of its digits is different.

6. Three of its digits are multiples of 2.

7. It has only one odd digit.

8. Its hundreds digit is its smallest digit.

9. Its largest digit is 8.

10. Its tens digit is 2.

Puzzle 40

1. It is a five-digit whole number.

2. Its hundreds digit and its tens digit are the same.

3. Its ten thousands digit and its ones digit are the same.

4. It has only one 4.

5. The sum of its hundreds digit and its ten thousands digit is 8.

6. The product of its thousands digit and its hundreds digit is 0.

7. All of its digits are even.

8. Its ones digit is twice its thousands digit.

9. Its tens digit is 0.

10. Its thousands digit is 4.

Puzzle 41

1. It is a six-digit whole number.

2. It has only two different digits, each used three times.

3. The product of its hundred thousands digit and its hundreds digit is 12.

4. It is greater than 500,000.

5. The sum of its thousands digit and its hundreds digit is 8.

6. The difference between its hundreds digit and its ones digit is 0.

7. The quotient of its thousands digit and its tens digit is 1.

8. The product of its ten thousands digit and its ones digit is 4.

9. The difference between its thousands digit and its ones digit is 4.

10. Its hundreds digit is 2.

Puzzle 42

1. It is a six-digit whole number.

2. Its only digits are 0 and 2.

3. The sum of all of its digits is 8.

4. It is divisible by 5.

5. The product of its hundred thousands digit and its tens digit divided by its thousands digit is 2.

6. The sum of its thousands digit and its hundreds digit is 2.

7. It is greater than 200,000.

8. The sum of its hundred thousands digit, its ten thousands digit, and its thousands digit is 6.

9. Its tens digit is 2.

10. Its ones digit is 0.

Puzzle 43

1. It is a four-digit whole number.

2. It has three different digits.

3. The product of all of its digits is 81.

4. Its hundreds digit is greater than 4.

5. It is an odd number.

6. Its hundreds digit is the product of its tens digit and its ones digit.

7. Its thousands digit is less than its hundreds digit.

8. The sum of all of its digits is 16.

9. Its hundreds digit is 9.

10. Its tens digit is 3.

Puzzle 44

1. It is a three-digit whole number.

2. Its hundreds digit is its largest digit.

3. Its ones digit is its only digit that is not divisible by 3.

4. None of its digits are 0.

5. Its tens digit is one-third of its hundreds digit.

6. It has a remainder of 2 when it is divided by 8.

7. It is an even number.

8. The difference between its ones digit and its tens digit is 5.

9. The difference between its hundreds digit and its ones digit is 1.

10. Its tens digit is 3.

Puzzle 45

1. It is a six-digit whole number.

2. It has only one odd digit.

3. It has only one even digit.

4. It is greater than 580,000.

5. It is less than 600,000.

6. It is an even number.

7. The quotient of its hundred thousands digit and its tens digit is 1.

8. Its digits alternate.

9. The sum of its ten thousands digit and its thousands digit is 13.

10. Its hundreds digit is 8.

Puzzle 46

1. It is a four-digit whole number.

2. Its ones digit is an odd number.

3. Its tens digit is one-fourth of its thousands digit.

4. The product of all of its digits is 0.

5. Its ones digit is less than its tens digit.

6. The sum of all of its digits is 11.

7. It is greater than 8000.

8. It has only one odd digit.

9. Its hundreds digit is 0.

10. Its tens digit is 2.

Puzzle 47

1. It is a four-digit whole number.

2. Each digit is greater than the digit to its right.

3. It is greater than 9000.

4. Its thousands digit is the sum of its hundreds digit and its tens digit.

5. It is an odd number.

6. Its tens digit is the difference between its hundreds digit and its ones digit.

7. It has only one even digit.

8. The product of its hundreds digit and its ones digit is 5.

9. Its ones digit is 1.

10. Its tens digit is 4.

Puzzle 48

1. It is a four-digit whole number.

2. The product of its thousands digit and its hundreds digit is 3.

3. The product of its tens digit and its ones digit is 0.

4. The product of its thousands digit and its ones digit is 24.

5. It is an even number.

6. Its hundreds digit is greater than its tens digit.

7. Its hundreds digit is less than its ones digit.

8. The difference between its thousands digit and its tens digit is 3.

9. Its ones digit is 8.

10. Its hundreds digit is 1.

Puzzle 49

1. It is a three-digit whole number.

2. All of its digits are different.

3. One of its digits differs from each of its other two digits by 1.

4. Its tens digit is its smallest digit.

5. The difference between its ones digit and its tens digit is 2.

6. The sum of its largest digit and its smallest digit is 12.

7. It has two odd digits.

8. It is greater than 600.

9. Its ones digit is 7.

10. Its tens digit is 5.

Puzzle 50

1. It is a three-digit whole number.

2. Its remainder is 4 if it is divided by 5.

3. Its tens digit is a divisor of 11.

4. Its hundreds digit is 1 less than a multiple of 3.

5. It has no even digits.

6. Its hundreds digit is 4 less than its ones digit.

7. The sum of all of its digits is 15.

8. The product of its tens digit and its ones digit is 9.

9. Its tens digit is 1.

10. Its hundreds digit is 5.

Puzzle 51

1. It is a five-digit whole number.

2. It is divisible by 5.

3. It is less than 80,000.

4. It is greater than 77,000.

5. Its hundreds digit is the product of its tens digit and its ones digit.

6. None of its digits are even.

7. It has only three different digits.

8. Two of its digits have a difference of 2.

9. Two of its digits have a difference of 4.

10. Its tens digit is 1.

Puzzle 52

1. It is a four-digit whole number.

2. Its ones digit has exactly two factors.

3. Its tens digit has exactly one factor.

4. Its hundreds digit has exactly three factors.

5. Its thousands digit is the product of its hundreds digit and its tens digit.

6. The sum of all of its digits is less than 12.

7. It has only one odd digit.

8. Two of its digits are the same.

9. Its ones digit divides its thousands digit.

10. Its tens digit is 1.

Puzzle 53

1. It is a four-digit whole number.

2. It is a multiple of 25.

3. Its hundreds digit is 2 more than its tens digit.

4. Its thousands digit is 1 less than its tens digit.

5. Two of its digits are multiples of 3.

6. It has only one even digit.

7. Its hundreds digit is its largest digit.

8. Its thousands digit is not its smallest digit.

9. Its smallest digit is 5.

10. Its tens digit is 7.

Challenge Puzzle I

1. It is a four-digit whole number.

2. The product of all of its digits is 16.

3. The product of two of its digits is 4.

4. It is an even number.

5. Its thousands digit and its ones digit are the same.

6. Its hundreds digit and its tens digit are the same.

7. The sum of three of its digits is 6.

8. The product of three of its digits is 8.

9. Its hundreds digit is 2.

10. All of its digits are the same.

Challenge Puzzle II

1. It is a four-digit whole number.

2. The product of all of its digits is 24.

3. The product of two of its digits is 4.

4. It is an odd number.

5. Its thousands digit and its hundreds digit are the same.

6. The product of three of its digits is 12.

7. The sum of three of its digits is 6.

8. Its tens digit is less than its ones digit.

9. Its hundreds digit is 2.

10. Three of its digits are the same.

Solutions to the Puzzles

The clue number given by the solution is the first clue in the sequence at which the solution to the puzzle can be determined.

1.	541, Clue 6	21.	683, Clue 7	41.	626,262, Clue 7
2.	2637, Clue 6	22.	95,102, Clue 6	42.	222,020, Clue 6
3.	3415, Clue 6	23.	179,719, Clue 8	43.	1933, Clue 6
4.	808, Clue 8	24.	812, Clue 7	44.	938, Clue 6
5.	6886, Clue 6	25.	15,315, Clue 6	45.	585,858, Clue 8
6.	2237, Clue 5	26.	881,181, Clue 7	46.	8021, Clue 5
7.	178, Clue 5	27.	101,110, Clue 6	47.	9541, Clue 6
8.	494, Clue 7	28.	1824, Clue 7	48.	3108, Clue 4
9.	9311, Clue 5	29.	365, Clue 6	49.	657, Clue 6
10.	314, Clue 7	30.	223, Clue 7	50.	519, Clue 5
11.	842,284, Clue 8	31.	292,929, Clue 8	51.	77,515, Clue 7
12.	139, Clue 7	32.	4103, Clue 5	52.	4412, Clue 6
13.	374, Clue 6	33.	1347, Clue 6	53.	6975, Clue 5
14.	1455, Clue 5	34.	1057, Clue 4	I.	2222, Clue 8
15.	440, Clue 8	35.	564, Clue 6	II.	2223, Clue 7
16.	9797, Clue 5	36.	268, Clue 5		
17.	5412, Clue 5	37.	40,004, Clue 8		
18.	981, Clue 5	38.	1778, Clue 6		
19.	989, Clue 7	39.	8025, Clue 5		
20.	8620, Clue 5	40.	84,008, Clue 6		